Smudge a
Chewpen
Sentence Book

Paul Groves and
Nigel Grimshaw

Edward Arnold

First published 1981
by Edward Arnold (Publishers) Ltd
41 Bedford Square, London WC1B 3DQ

British Library Cataloguing in Publication Data
Groves, Paul
Smudge and chewpen sentence book.
1. English language – Grammar – Problems, exercises etc.
I. Title II. Grimshaw, Nigel
428'.2 PE1112

ISBN 0-7131-0510-0

Text set in IBM 11/12 pt Press Roman by TA Tek-Art, Croydon, Surrey.
Printed in Great Britain by Spottiswoode Ballantyne Limited,
Colchester and London

Contents

Joining three sentences

Joining four sentences

To the teacher

After spelling mistakes, nothing seems to cause teachers more concern than unpunctuated work. The creative writing surge has produced a great deal of very interesting work from children, full of feeling and sensitivity. But all too frequently it is unpunctuated because the pupil does not understand the pattern of the English sentence.

The aim of this book is to give the pupil understanding through a tremendous amount of practice at first of writing the simple sentence. Work then progresses to the complex sentence. As few grammatical terms as possible are used throughout the book.

By the end of the course it is hoped that creative writing will be improved in that the pupil will have the confidence to write longer sentences correctly.

Looking at the sentence

1

Capital letter and full-stop

Jim Smudge was writing about a football match:

> it was a good match the play went from end to end three goals had been scored already Brighouse had scored two for United he was their striker then came this funny moment in the match Brighouse slipped in the mud the Rovers goalkeeper took the ball from him and punted it down the field the United goalkeeper came out to catch it to his surprise a gust of wind took it over his head and it went straight into the net

Mr Wright looked at it. 'I thought we'd cleared this up,' he said. 'Where are the capital letters and full-stops to show the sentences?'

'I forgot,' said Jim. 'When it gets exciting I forget.'

'You mustn't forget,' replied Mr Wright, 'otherwise you'll find yourself writing nonsense. You normally write for someone else to read your work. They must understand clearly what you mean. They can't unless your sentences are marked off clearly.

'I think I'd better give you a course on sentences. First of all:

A sentence must begin with a capital letter and end with a full-stop.

'Now here are your sentences. I've written them out separately. Begin each one with a capital letter and end each one with a full-stop.'

a Do this with Jim:

1 it was a good match
2 the play went from end to end
3 three goals had been scored already

4 Brighouse had scored two for United
5 he was their striker
6 then came a funny moment in the match
7 Brighouse slipped in the mud
8 the Rovers goalkeeper took the ball from him
9 he punted it down the field
10 the United goalkeeper came out to catch it
11 to his surprise a gust of wind took it over his head
12 it went straight into the net

b Here are some more individual sentences to punctuate with Jim:

1 the ghost haunted the house
2 i like chocolate
3 she goes to work at eight o'clock
4 he was fishing under the bridge
5 the monster struck at midnight
6 give me two of them
7 they say you should not go there
8 he lives near the railway station
9 i am not going to help you
10 a shiver ran down her back
11 don't ask me to help you again
12 my family are moving to a new town miles away

c Here is another piece of continuous writing divided up into sentences like Jim's football piece. Punctuate them:

1 the girl went to the house
2 it was creepy-looking with shutters on the windows
3 the door creaked open slowly
4 it revealed a dark passage
5 she crept in
6 a cobweb brushed her face
7 then something ran across her feet
8 she put her hand to her mouth
9 she knew she must not scream
10 she found her torch
11 she switched it on
12 a dead body lay at her feet

13 the skull was showing beneath the skin

Now write this out again as a paragraph.

Your own sentences
In a paragraph write about ten sentences on one of these:

a haunted house
saving a drowning person
how I spent last Saturday

NB Remember, 'He' and 'She' normally begin sentences.

Additional exercise
Punctuate the following into sentences:

one day Jim went on a cross-country race he had to run five miles first of all he had to cross three fields he had a shock in the first one it had a bull in it it chased him the second one was a ploughed field he slipped about in the mud and fell over three times in the mud he looked like a monster the third one was full of blackberry bushes which scratched his legs then he had to go through a wood he nearly knocked himself out on a low branch he decided he would never do this again but when he got back to school the master told him he had won jim was very pleased perhaps it was not such a bad sport after all

2
The question mark

Anne Chewpen had a go at the haunted house piece of writing. Mr Wright looked at it:

> The house was eerie. Creepers covered the outside. Jane slowly opened the creaking door. What was that. Was somebody in the house. There was a low moan coming from the upstairs room. Dare she go up. Her heart was beating rapidly. Did she have the courage to mount the stairs. She decided she must. The stairs creaked like the door. She stopped on the fifth one. Why was she really here. What was the mystery of this place. Who owned it. She must go up and find out.

'Very exciting,' said Mr Wright, 'but there's just one point.'

'It's punctuated in sentences,' said Anne. 'I have put in a capital letter at the beginning and a full-stop at the end.'

'It's just that some of your sentences are questions, Anne. A question must have a question mark over the full-stop. Have a go at these.'

a Punctuate the following individual sentences correctly. Some are ordinary sentences. Some are questions:

1 is it going to be a fine day
2 i am going to France
3 can I help you
4 blood oozed from a deep wound in his arm
5 we must keep Britain tidy
6 who was that I saw you with last night
7 which one do you fancy
8 are you really fourteen
9 I would like ten of them

10 catch one of them for me
11 did you feel a cobweb brush across your face
12 the dustmen are coming down the road
13 the plane swooped low over the houses
14 the books were on the shelves
15 have you seen my mother
16 why are you ringing up your uncle
17 several men were waiting round the corner
18 shall I go and help mother with the washing-up
19 as it is raining I am not going to the picnic
20 were any of the answers right

Now write out Anne's piece again. Put in any question marks that are needed.

b Here is Jim's attempt at the drowning piece. Put in the missing capital letters, full-stops and question marks:

> what was that out at sea was it a plastic air-bed yes it was a small boy was clinging to it how could Jim save him the tide was going out fast he dived in he swam towards it it was too far out he turned back would he be able to reach the beach it was a struggle what could he do now there was the lifeguard he ran towards him a boat was launched the small boy was saved just in time the lifeguard told Jim off for risking his own life

Your own sentences
Write down the following:

three questions you could ask a doctor
three questions you could ask in a shop
five questions your family could ask at breakfast
five questions you would like to ask your favourite pop star

Remember, useful question words are: who, what, why, how, when and where.

If you write speech in any of your stories it will probably have questions and answers in it. It is the same for plays as well.

3
Making sense

Jim was writing. 'Look!' he said to Mr Wright, 'I've put in all the the capital letters and full-stops.'

Mr Wright read it:

> It was midnight. 008 stood at the corner of the street. Under the lamplight. He slowly lit a cigarette. Because he was nervous. A shot rang out. A bullet struck the lamp-post. Near the base. If he had not moved as he flicked his lighter. It would have hit his face. He ducked to the ground.

'Just a minute,' said Mr Wright. 'I must tell you the next rule about a sentence: a sentence must make sense. You've punctuated pieces of writing that are parts of other sentences and don't make sense on their own.'

For instance:

under the lamplight
if he had not moved as he flicked his lighter

Neither of these is a sentence. The sentence should read:

008 stood at the corner of the street under the lamplight. If he had not moved as he flicked his lighter, it would have hit his face.

As you can see you can't judge a sentence by the number of words. You can have a short sentence like: 'A shot rang out.' that makes sense. You can also have long groups of words that don't make sense and need other words added.

Always ask: does what I have punctuated as a sentence make sense?

a Here are some groups of words. Some of them are sentences and some are not. Write out the sentences only, correctly punctuated. Remember, a question is a sentence.

1 the miser counted his money
2 in the front
3 although it was raining
4 because the vampire would not go away
5 it was raining
6 by the side of the large shop
7 up in the air
8 as well as he could
9 which was not helping him much
10 the ghost would appear soon
11 i can go
12 the goalkeeper dived to the left
13 when I am late
14 running down the road
15 he was fourteen
16 sitting on the green fence
17 that was in the middle of the main road by the bridge
18 the aeroplane crashed in the field
19 since it was raining
20 over the moon
21 can I help you
22 will you be going out
23 the boss sacked him
24 there were ten of them in the team
25 if you find a body there

b Now take the groups of words you decided were not sentences. Add words to them to make them into sentences. Here are two done for you:

In the front of the queue was a small girl.
Although it was raining he still went out.

Your own sentences
Write out five sentences about a rainy day. Then mix them with five groups of words that are not sentences. Get your neighbour to:

1 Decide which are the sentences.
2 Then add words to the non-sentences to make them sensible.

Additional exercise

Punctuate this correctly into sentences: NB 'And' does not normally begin a sentence.

> Anne was going down the road. By the river. On the bridge were two women one had a baby. In a pram. She was a very large woman. With a big hat on. They were both eating ice-cream. The smaller woman was trying to give ice-cream to the baby. The baby did not want it he kept crying. And pushing the ice-cream away. The big woman then tried she made funny faces. At the baby. The baby screamed even more. And kicked off his blankets. The blankets fell. In the mud. They got dirty. Because it had been raining all day. This made the big woman cross she waved her arms about the top flew off her ice-cream. And hit the small woman. In the face this knocked off her glasses. She screamed. As the ice-cream ran all down her coat. Then they both laughed. And the baby laughed as well.

4
The Subject

'What are you really doing when you write a sentence?' asked Anne.

'That's interesting,' said Mr Wright. 'Let's take the simple sentence first. In the simple sentence you write about one thing. If you wrote: *Dogs* like bones. You would be telling me one thing about dogs. The word *dogs* would become the *subject* of the sentence.'

Here are three more simple sentences:

I am fourteen.
He went to Wembley last Saturday.
The policeman caught a burglar.

In each case you are writing one thing about the subject.

a What are the subjects of these sentences? Write them out and underline the subjects:

1 The fisherman caught a pike.
2 She mistook the price of the dress.
3 They did not get in.
4 The motorist had a puncture.
5 He sat on a drawing pin.
6 The invaders destroyed the town.

b Now write sentences of your own about:

1 Cats . . .
2 The lion . . .
3 The book . . .
4 A house . . .
5 He . . .

6 They . . .
7 She . . .
8 You . . .
9 I . . .
10 The climber . . .

Did you write one thing about each subject? Check.

Sometimes you have a describing word about the subject:

The fisherman caught a fish.
becomes:
The old fisherman caught a fish.

The man was surprised.
The red-faced man was surprised.

c Add a describing word to these subjects:

1 The. . .monster chased Dr Who.
2 The . . . house was creepy.
3 A . . . boy cut his thumb.
4 Those . . . dogs have chased the postman.
5 The . . . swimmer crossed the Channel.

You can also have a group of words to describe a subject. This lengthens the simple sentence even more:

The fisherman under the bridge caught a pike.
The girl with the limp walked one hundred kilometres.

d Add describing words to these: make sure it is more than one word:

1 The boy with . . . was sent home.
2 The team at . . . lost again.
3 The tree by . . . has Dutch elm disease.
4 The chalet under . . . was covered in snow.
5 The boat in . . . was sinking fast.
6 The garden over . . . was very beautiful.
7 The house round . . . is on fire.
8 The cafe up . . . is closing down.
9 The car near . . . is blocking the road.

10 The cottage beside . . . is up for sale.

Your own sentences
Write five simple sentences about a fair. Underline the subject of of each sentence. Then see if you can add a describing word or words to the subject. Do not use, I, he, she, it, you or they as the subjects.

Additional exercise
Punctuate the following piece of writing. Then underline the subjects and any words that describe the subjects:

the lion went through the bush the heavy rain was still falling the king of the beasts did not like it it preferred the hot dry weather a thorn was sticking in its foot as well hunger was deep within it the lion had not eaten for a week a great roar came from it

the man with the camera was up a tree he was hoping to get a shot of a lion his camera had a tele-photo lens on it his wife was in a mini-bus nearby the unhappy lion broke cover she shouted as she saw it the man in the tree swung round quickly he slipped as he did so and fell out of the tree the hungry lion sprang at him the terrified woman raised her gun but she was too late to save him she fainted at the sight a game warden found her and the remains of the man one hour later

5
Revision

'Here is some revision for you,' said Mr Wright.

Do this with Jim and Anne.

a Punctuate these sentences correctly. Beware! Some are questions:

1 it was a sunny day yesterday
2 who were you with yesterday
3 give me that box
4 the creature had hairy scales all over it
5 the clock has not gone since yesterday
6 how many are going
7 can you see out of the window
8 the floor needs a good clean
9 why are you not going to the match
10 the earthquake caused many casualties

b Which of these groups of words make sentences? Copy them out correctly punctuated:

1 under the house
2 i am going home
3 by the side of the fountain
4 he caught fourteen fish in the canal
5 where are the others
6 blocking up the path
7 if I go tomorrow
8 which was bad for them
9 are you able to help me
10 over near the door

11 she soon caught a cold
12 because it was an old car
13 it kept the rain off him
14 he was only doing his best
15 the chair had a brown cover on it
16 why are you not helping me
17 when I am eighteen
18 the box was open
19 beside the M1
20 i like chips

Now add words to the groups of words that did not make sense to turn them into sentences.

c Write these sentences out and underline the subjects:

1 The car had a sun-top roof.
2 The house with the bay windows had an overgrown garden.
3 A hair-raising scream came from the room.
4 I will help my mother.
5 The beech tree was turning a golden brown.
6 He cannot help his sister.
7 She will not go skating.
8 The kiosk beside the pier sells candy floss.
9 A book of many pages will be needed.
10 A ghostly figure crept down the passage.

Your own sentences
Write five sentences about your birthday.
Write five sentences about being ill.
Write five sentences about your street.

6
Verbs

'Let me tell you another rule about sentences,' said Mr Wright to Jim: 'A sentence must have a verb in it.'

'What's a verb?' asked Jim.

'Let's take the easier ones first,' said Mr Wright. 'They are the 'doing' words in sentences.'

They are the words which make the sentences go:

The boy *kicked* the ball
The girl *ran* home.

Kicked and *ran* are the doing words of these sentences. They tell us about the action. See if you can spot the doing words in these sentences:

a Do this with Jim and Anne. Underline each verb:

1 The horse jumped over the fence.
2 A car smashed into a wall.
3 I write many letters.
4 He hurled the discus a record distance.
5 The plane flies very high.
6 I do not open other people's letters.
7 I often yawn during the maths lesson.
8 She gives him a pound on Sundays.
9 The police chased the gangsters' car.
10 The plant grew very tall.

b Complete these sentences by putting a verb in them:

1 He always . . . his mother on Sundays.
2 She . . . the rock over the cliff.
3 The pensioner . . . on the seat in the park.

4 The egg . . . off the table.
5 My grandfather . . . some beautiful carrots.
6 The boy . . . a fish in the lake.
7 She . . . herself to some more potatoes.
8 The policeman . . . the man's name in his book.
9 She . . . a pound from her brother.
10 The wrestler . . . his opponent out of the ring.

Your own sentences

Make sentences of your own by using these verbs:

went attacked sing marched stole helped wobbled found hobbled pushes learn caught take forget turned pulled stretches remember carried

Additional exercise

Punctuate the following piece into sentences. Then underline any verbs that you spot. NB 'by' 'in' 'for' 'down' 'up' and 'into' are not verbs:

the man fished by the canal he threw in the ground bait no fish came for it he sat down again it rained heavily he put up his big umbrella

a boy rode a bike along the tow-path he peddled hard he bent his head over the handlebars the bike crashed into the fisherman the boy shot over the handlebars he fell into the canal he shouted for help the man dived in he swam to the boy the boy struggled the man gripped him hard he saved him

7
Being and having verbs

'There are two very important verbs which are not *doing* words,' Mr Wright told Jim. 'They are *being* and *having* verbs.'

They come in these disguises:

am are is was were has have had
has been had been have been

Notice how they still help other words to make a sentence:

I *am* sixteen.
They *were* a long way from home.
The girl *had* a bad time.

'I want you to underline the *being* and *having* verbs in these sentences,' said Mr Wright.

a Do this with Jim and Anne:

1 I am not quite sure.
2 He was a fool.
3 They were not in the room.
4 The players are a very happy crowd.
5 The girl is up a tree.
6 I have fourteen fish in the net.
7 He had a lovely garden before the storm.
8 It had been a long hot day.

b Put in a 'being' or a 'having' verb to make these sentences:

1 I . . . fifteen.
2 The player . . . in the goal mouth.
3 They . . . very sad at his death.
4 The visitors . . . in the castle.

5 The mountaineer . . . very brave.
6 I . . . a big ice cream.
7 They . . . a good time before it rained.
8 It . . . a long time since I saw you.
9 How . . . the show?
10 He . . . . . . to the pictures.
11 I . . . a soft spot in my heart for him.
12 You . . . the best player I know.
13 It . . . . . . a long hot day.
14 I . . . ten of them altogether.
15 The clown . . . in the ring.
16 The cyclists . . . . . . this way before.
17 The footballers . . . a long time in the manager's room.
18 I . . . sure you will like it.
19 He . . . a bad cold.
20 The shoppers . . . on their way home.

Additional exercise
Punctuate the following piece. Then underline the 'being' and 'having' verbs:

> I am not sure what happened i was on my own it was very dark there were clouds covering the moon and stars it had been a wet day i am not normally a coward it is a long time since i was afraid i have no explanation for what happened i do not know the reasons for it suddenly a white figure was on the path ahead the air had a tremendous chill in it a hand came from the figure it clutched my throat i screamed and fell then there was nothing i have been afraid ever since

8

Time in sentences

Anne was doing some writing:

> It was a happy sight on the beach. Children playing in the sand. Dads fetching ice-cream. Mums drinking tea from thermos flasks. Grans knitting. Out at sea boats sailing. Massive waves breaking on the beach and foam running up the sand like probing fingers.

Mr Wright looked over her shoulder.

'It's good, sir,' said Anne. 'Isn't it?'

'Yes,' said Mr Wright. 'It's very promising. There's just one thing wrong though.'

'Oh, no!' sighed Anne. 'It's written in sentences. They've got verbs in them. Look: playing, fetching, drinking. They are all doing words.'

'Yes,' said Mr Wright. 'But in a proper sentence a verb must have a time to it.'

'Time?' queried Anne.

'Yes. You must know whether the action took place in the present, past or future time. When you say "children playing in the sand" you do not say when they are playing.'

'Well, it was last summer so I suppose I mean it to be in the past.'

'Then you must say "children played",' said Mr Wright. 'You could also say "children were playing" but more of that later. Here are some verbs in the present time. I want you to make them refer to past time. You will notice that some change and some add "ed" when they refer to past time.'

Do this with Jim and Anne:

Here is an example:

I help with the tea. Present.

I helped with the tea.	Past.
The man finds a Roman coin.	Present.
The man found a Roman coin.	Past.

Now do these:

1 I walk over the hill.
2 The tramp sits on a seat.
3 The policemen stop the traffic.
4 I catch the ball.
5 Her mother forgets the birthday every year.
6 Her brother sees her every day.
7 I suffer a great deal.
8 The boy reads the book.
9 The girl skips over the rope.
10 The gardener clips the hedge of the manor.
11 The actress takes her part well.
12 The referee spots the foul.
13 The boxer fights very well.
14 A horse gallops over the hill.
15 I stick new stamps in my album on Saturday.
16 He soon fences in the garden.
17 The fond mother pats the baby on the head.
18 She quickly drinks the medicine.
19 The small boy breaks the window.
20 The athlete jumps over the water jump.

9
Helping verbs

'I want to tell you more about the *being* and *having* verbs,' said Mr Wright. 'As well as being verbs on their own they can also help other verbs in a sentence. You could have said: "children were playing in the sand". That would have been in the past time. For the present time you could say "children are playing in the sand".'

Remember the disguises of the 'being' verb:

am   is   are   was   were

Put a helping verb into these sentences. Say after each sentence whether it is past or present time.

a Do this with Jim and Anne:

1 I . . . going to the seaside.
2 The train . . . coming down the track.
3 The ball . . . floating into the net.
4 The people . . . crowding into the match.
5 The houses . . . falling down.
6 I . . . looking for my friends.
7 She . . . complaining about the tights.
8 He . . . realising a dream.
9 The cyclists . . . pedalling hard.
10 The eggs . . . lying on the grass.

Now go back and write Anne's piece on page 25 out twice, once in the present time and once in the past time.

Then there were the disguises for the 'having' verb:

has   have   had
Use them to form a past time in these sentences.

b Do this with Jim and Anne:

1 I . . . pinched my finger.
2 The woman . . . trapped the spy.
3 The policeman . . . discovered the secret weapon.
4 I . . . caught a fish in the pond.
5 He . . . taken all the money.
6 They . . . helped his mother a great deal.
7 It . . . cost him his life.
8 The Indians . . . roamed the plains for many years.
9 The secretary . . . written a long letter to the boss.
10 It . . . seemed a very long winter this year.

Your own sentences
Write five sentences about going to the dentist in the past.
Write five sentences about cooking in the past or the present.
Write five sentences about playing a game in the past or present.

Additional exercise
Punctuate the following piece. Then underline the verbs and their helping verbs:

> the woman was walking by the sea she had been going for three hours she was feeling very tired she sat down near a rock suddenly the sea by the rock was beginning to bubble the sea was foaming two heads were coming out of the water she was horrified by the giant mouths one mouth was holding a seal it had caught the seal by the head it was chewing it its teeth were chomping like a great machine it had happened too quickly for her to panic suddenly the monsters were diving fast they had seen the woman for some reason they were frightened of her

10
Revision

'Here is some more revision for you to do,' said Mr Wright

Do this with Jim and Anne:

a Write out these sentences and underline the verbs:

1 The girl sat on the settee.
2 The butterfly settled on the cabbage.
3 The duke flies to Australia tomorrow.
4 The forester cut down the tree.
5 I discussed the programme with him.
6 The ball pitched near the wicket.
7 You open the tin for me.
8 He grew to be a tall young man.
9 She missed her mother a great deal.
10 The paper boy always fetches it for him.

b Complete these sentences by putting a verb in them:

1 The car . . . out of control.
2 The swimmer . . . at the deep end.
3 I . . . you will get better.
4 The burglar . . . the lady's jewels.
5 The TV announcer . . . the news
6 The music centre . . . on fire.
7 The egg . . . off the table.
8 The poacher . . . the deer in the forest.
9 Grandma . . . the new jersey.
10 The gardener . . . up the leaves from the orchard.

c Make sentences of your own using these verbs:

kills conquered surprised squandered witnessed
spoilt fries burned flowed whispered

d Underline the 'being' and 'having' verbs in these sentences:

1 He was under the lorry.
2 What is the right answer?
3 I am hopeful today.
4 The actors are in the green room.
5 They were sure of the question.
6 The jockeys have two saddles.
7 It has seven compartments.
8 The travellers had a bumpy ride.
9 It has been wonderful for them.
10 This year has been the best yet.

e Put in a 'being' or 'having' verb to make these sentences:

1 It . . . on the television.
2 He . . . . . . to China.
3 The children . . . in the way.
4 The butcher . . . in the shop.
5 I . . . very hurt.
6 There . . . fifteen of them in the team.
7 The grass . . . a lot greener.
8 It . . . . . . the work of a life time
9 She . . . too tall for the job.
10 What . . . the best tablets?

f Put these into past tense. Do not use a 'being' or 'having' verb:

1 I believe in freedom.
2 He breaks everything.
3 The branch touches the window sometimes.
4 The builder builds very quickly.
5 That trick deceives most people.
6 She soon opens the parcel.
7 The athlete runs a mile in record time.

8 She hurries down the hill.
9 The cook cracks the egg.
10 That takes the biscuit.

g Put a helping verb into these sentences. Say after each whether it is past or present time:

1 She . . . hoping to go to college.
2 The red balloon . . . floating over the pier.
3 The team . . . losing the match.
4 The boy . . . dreaming of becoming a star.
5 Her parents . . . moving on Tuesday.
6 I . . . seeing the doctor tomorrow.
7 The house by the river . . . falling down.
8 The moon . . . hiding behind a cloud.
9 The hen . . . sitting on the eggs.
10 You . . . going to help me find the answer.

h Make this (1) into past time, (2) into present time:

People streaming into the stadium. Programme-sellers selling programmes. Boys looking for their mates. All the home team supporters wearing their scarves. Some of them chanting. Policemen stopping people getting crushed.

i Put a helping verb in to help form these sentences:

1 I . . . caught a cold.
2 The bandsmen . . . won the contest.
3 She . . . ridden the horse for many hours.
4 It . . . been the most happy day of my life.
5 She . . . rubbed all the shine off it.
6 I . . . glimpsed someone like him before.
7 The student . . . missed the train by two minutes.
8 You . . . been told the truth.

11
Extending sentences – when

Jim was writing:

> The man went down the street. He had his hat pushed down. He looked suspicious. A policeman looked at him. The man pretended to look into a shop window. A dog came up. It sniffed round his legs. Then it began to bark.

Mr Wright looked at it. 'Good,' he said, 'you're punctuating well. What I want to do now is to help you extend your sentences. You can have longer sentences providing you obey the rules. Let's look at your first sentence: "The man went down the street." Now ask yourself the question: When?'

'Yesterday,' replied Jim.

'Well, that's one word,' said Mr Wright, 'but we could try adding more than one. How about: "The man went down the street last Tuesday?" How about: "The man went down the street in the small hours of the morning?" '

'I like that last one,' said Jim.

'When we add a group of words like that with no time verb in it we call it a phrase. I want you to add some phrases to these sentences. Each time ask yourself: When? Start your phrase with *in* or *at* or *on* or *by*. Do not start *when*.'

Do this with Jim and Anne:

1 The swan built its nest . . .
2 Leaves fall off the trees . . .
3 It thundered . . .
4 I have to get to work . . .
5 The train departs from the station . . .
6 The woman cycled to Southend . . .
7 008 trapped the criminals . . .
8 It is always hot . . .

9 He fell in the river . . .
10 The supporter went to the football match . . .
11 The hand fell off the clock . . .
12 She broke her arm . . .
13 Dad got home from work . . .
14 We often get snow . . .
15 My sister got married . . .
16 The fighter plane was shot down . . .
17 The new house will be ready . . .
18 I do not like to be out alone . . .
19 England could win the World Cup . . .
20 The television would not work . . .
21 The fire was put out . . .
22 The rally car crashed . . .
23 My mother will have a new baby . . .
24 He slipped on a banana skin . . .
25 The heavy rains always come . . .

'We can vary our sentences, said Mr Wright, 'by putting the phrase first.'

In the small hours of the morning the man went down the street.

Do this with all the sentences you have just written.

12
Extending sentences – where, how and why

'There are other questions you can ask yourself, to extend sentences,' said Mr Wright. 'The question: Where? for example. Take the sentence: I saw the football match. We could add: I saw the football match *in the new stadium*. We have done this by asking ourselves: Where?'

Use these words to introduce these phrases: in, at, by, near, beside, to, over, under, on.

Add phrases to these sentences by asking yourself: Where?

a Do this with Jim and Anne:

1 We went on holiday . . .
2 The poacher caught a trout . . .
3 There was a great deal of dust . . .
4 The monster roamed the plains . . .
5 The postman delivered the letter . . .
6 England won the test match . . .
7 They had a splendid meal . . .
8 The spaceship zoomed upwards . . .
9 The boys and girls cycled quickly . . .
10 He threw the ball . . .

You will find you can reverse some of the sentences by putting the phrase first.

Do this with those that sound sensible.

With these sentences ask yourselves the question: how?

Here is an example:

The boy answered the teacher.
The boy answered the teacher *in a rude manner*.

You may want to put just one word ending in 'ly'. You can avoid this by starting with 'by', 'in' or 'with'.

b Make sure you answer the question: how?

1 He scored a goal . . .
2 The car crashed into the tree . . .
3 The fireman fell off the roof . . .
4 The soldiers fought the battle . . .
5 My grandfather walked to work . . .
6 The woman sat on the wet seat . . .
7 He slipped on the ice . . .
8 She was helping her grandmother . . .
9 They were playing the music . . .
10 The lady pushed the pram . . .

Now reverse some of your sentences that sound sensible by putting the phrase first.

Now add phrases to these sentences by asking yourself the question: why? NB Sometimes we use a verb with no time.

Here is an example:

He ran to the fire station.
He ran to the fire station *to raise the alarm.*

c Begin each phrase with 'to' or 'for':

1 The murderer went to the house . . .
2 The boy sat by the river . . .
3 The girl dived into the canal . . .
4 Grandpa dug the garden . . .
5 The forester chopped down the tree . . .
6 He read the book . . .
7 The king built the castle . . .
8 The potholer struck a match . . .
9 The mother punished the child . . .
10 The wrestler pinned down his opponent . . .

Now reverse any of these that sound sensible by putting the phrase first.

13
Extending sentences – further

'My sentences are still not as long as some of those in the books I read,' said Anne.

'All in good time,' said Mr Wright. 'There is still some more work on phrases. You can ask yourself more than one question to extend a sentence.'

Take the sentence: Dad cooks the meal. You could ask yourself: When and Where?

Dad cooks the meal *at dinner time in the kitchen.*

or

At dinner time Dad cooks the meal *in the kitchen.*

Ask yourself When? and Where? to extend these sentences.

a Do this with Jim and Anne. Check back on the introductory words:

1 The boy kicked the ball.
2 Gran was eating her meal.
3 Dad walked the dog.
4 Auntie knitted a sweater.
5 Grandad sat on a bench.
6 The man put up a poster.
7 Gary caught a fish.
8 Mary started a quarrel.
9 John found a bike.
10 Dad mended the car.

Now ask yourselves: when? and how?

Here is an example:

The army moved off.

It could be:

The army moved off *at dawn* in *great secrecy.*

or

In great secrecy the army moved *off at dawn.*

b Now do these. Check on the introductory words first. Use a word ending in 'ly' if you cannot think of a phrase for: how?

1 The plane flew from the airport.
2 The burglar stole from the flat.
3 He ate his egg.
4 She washed her jumper.
5 The monster knocked down the house.
6 The ghost haunted the room.
7 The bowler bowled the ball.
8 The woman swept the stairs.
9 She played a record.
10 He stubbed out his cigarette.

Now ask yourselves: where? And how? Only use an 'ly' word if you cannot think of a phrase for: how?

Here is an example:

The motorbike roared.
The motorbike roared *round the track in a great growl of sound.*

or

In a great growl of sound the motorbike *roared round the track.*

c now do these:

1 The car came.
2 The train whistled.
3 The dog barked.
4 The man ran.
5 The cake was cooked.
6 The dinner was burned.
7 She came downstairs.
8 The girl jumped.
9 He caught a fish.

10 The engineer built a bridge.

Now ask yourselves: when? And why? Check on the introductory words.

Here is an example:

I bought a lawnmower.
Two years ago I bought a lawnmower *to cut my mother's lawn*

d Now do these

1 He sold his bike.
2 She went to France.
3 The sailor caught a bus.
4 She divided a bar of chocolate.
5 The chimpanzee pushed its mate.
6 The diver searched the wreck.
7 The postman went up the hill.
8 An ant crawled across the garden path.
9 The farmer ploughed the field.
10 The baker made the cake.

Now ask yourselves: where? And why?

Here is an example:

The man washed his clothes.
The man washed his clothes *at the launderette to be smart at the wedding.*

e Now do these:

1 The teacher looked at the book.
2 The plumber mended the pipe.
3 The secretary typed the letter.
4 The engine driver stopped the train.
5 The miner moved the rock.
6 A doctor called at the house.
7 The bull chased across the field.
8 The rent collector visited the flats.
9 The eagle swooped to the ground.
10 The young boy bought a present.

Now ask yourselves: how? And why?

Here is an example?

The girl wrote a letter.
In great secrecy the girl wrote a letter *to tell her boyfriend the news.*

f Now do these:

1 The prisoner climbed the wall.
2 The bandmen blew their bugles.
3 The teacher spoke to the girl.
4 The elephant rampaged through the jungle.
5 The driver pushed the van.
6 The sheriff rounded up the gunmen.
7 The Indian lay on the bed of nails.
8 The policeman opened the parcel.
9 The butcher cut the meat.
10 The professor looked at the code.

Check the sentences you have written in this section. Could you ask yourselves three questions to extend any of them? For example: how? Why? And when?

Your own sentences
Write sentences round these verbs. Underline any phrases you use:

speaks opened turned was going had helped secured tricked steals were moving had removed

14
Adding descriptive words and phrases

'Before we leave the simple sentence there is one more way we can lengthen it,' said Mr Wright. 'It is also a way of making it more interesting. We can improve and enjoy our writing by adding descriptive words and phrases.'

Take this sentence: The man came down the road.

We could add descriptive words when we think about describing the man and the road. It could be:

The scruffy man came down the twisting road.

Or we could add more than one descriptive word:

The tall, scruffy man came down the muddy, twisting road.
(Note the commas to separate the descriptive words.)

We could improve the sentence by adding descriptive phrases:

The man with the limp came down the road by the bridge.

Or we could add both:

The tall, scruffy man with the limp came down the muddy, twisting road by the bridge.

In the following sentences add single descriptive words where you see three dots:

a Do this with Jim and Anne:

1 The . . . knight saved the . . . maiden.
2 The . . . house is by the . . . river.
3 The . . . boy kicked the . . . can.
4 The . . . monster roamed the . . . forest.
5 The . . . rain ruined the . . . bonfire.
6 The . . . curtains were hung in the . . . room.
7 The . . . car crashed into the . . . gate.

8 The . . . shop sold . . . potatoes.
9 A . . . lady sat on a . . . seat.
10 The . . . chimney fell on the . . . garage.

b Now add more than one descriptive word where you see the dots: Remember to divide them with a comma:

1 The . . . egg should not have been sold.
2 The . . . laugh of my uncle made my aunt ashamed.
3 The . . . clock was worth a thousand pounds.
4 A . . . runner came into view.
5 The . . . man caught a . . . fish.
6 The . . . tramp drank from the . . . bottle.
7 The . . . jungle hid the . . . gorilla.
8 The . . . sea swamped the . . . ship.
9 The . . . lorry slowed down in the . . . fog.
10 The . . . soldier climbed the . . . pole.

c Now add descriptive phrases where you see the dots. Useful introducing words are: with, by, in, over, near, beside, on, under under, at, of:

1 The man . . . gave a pound to the boy.
2 The tramp . . . had a dog with him.
3 The elephant . . . made a trumpeting sound.
4 A policeman . . . controlled the traffic.
5 The striker . . . scored a great goal.
6 The milkman . . . delivered the wrong number of bottles.
7 The house . . . is now empty.
8 The snake . . . attacked the monkey . . .
9 The dancer . . . won a prize . . .
10 The road . . . has too many houses . . .

Look at twenty of the sentences you have written in this 'simple sentence' section of the book.

Can you add any more descriptive words or phrases to any of them to make them longer sentences?

The compound sentence

15
Joining sentences – and

Anne was writing a piece for Mr Wright:

> I went down the road and I saw this tramp and he had very dirty clothes and he smelled terribly and I did not like to go near him.

'Look, sir,' she said. 'I've written a long sentence.'

'You have,' said Mr Wright, 'but I think it's time I warned you about using *and*. It's a very useful word and one of its uses is to join sentences together. But you must be sure that the ideas in the sentences are closely connected. It's also best, at your stage of English, to use only one *and* in sentence joining.'

It would have been better to have written:

> I went down the road and I saw this tramp. He had very dirty clothes and he smelled terribly. I did not like to go near him.

Write out these sentences and join them with *and* only if you think they are closely connected.

a Do this with Jim and Anne:

1 The parcel was an awkward shape. I could not wrap it up.
2 The elephants came down the trail. There are many elephants in Burma.
3 The girl cut her leg. It bled badly.
4 The policeman locked up the criminal. He had a stocking over his face.
5 Stop telling lies. Let me know the true story.
6 The farm had six cows. It had a tractor as well.
7 The barber cut the man's hair. It was six o'clock.
8 The striker scored a goal. The left-back ran up to congratulate him.

9 The waitress brought the meal. She had blonde hair.
10 He pushed out the boat. It caught on a rock.
11 China is a large country. It has a big population.
12 The moon was rising. Jim left the house.
13 The dentist took out two of his teeth. He felt bad all afternoon.
14 She had never been out with him before. It was a nice day.
15 Give me a new one. I hope it is not broken this time.

b Now add a closely connected sentence of your own to the following:

1 The butcher cut the meat and . . .
2 The winger scored a goal and . . .
3 The girl broke her arm and . . .
4 Dad cleaned the windows and . . .
5 The dog ate the seaweed and . . .
6 The teacher punished the girl and . . .
7 A car came round the corner and . . .
8 The ghost came through the wall and . . .
9 The school party went to France and . . .
10 She knocked the egg off the table and . . .

Your own sentences
Now, using 'and', join two sentences of your own together about these things:

a visit to the fair
Cleaning the house
Playing in the street
Doing your favourite sport
Getting dressed
Visiting a friend
Not sleeping
Your journey to school
Catching a cold
Going to the doctor

16
Joining sentences – but

'There are ways of avoiding *and*,' said Mr Wright. 'Any word repeated too much in English gets boring. I will show you some other words you can use in the next few lessons.'

Let's look at *but*:

I went out but it was a horrid day.

Here *but* is joining two sentences together.

Write out any of the following sentences that would suit being being joined together by *but*. Leave those which are not suitable or do not sound sensible.

a Do this with Jim and Anne:

1 He loves pop music. His brother-in-law does not.
2 She caught a cold. It had rained.
3 I do not like the cinema. I will go all the same.
4 He moved house to Peterborough. He had never been there before.
5 I shall not go to Greece. I might go to Turkey.
6 He moved the settee. The rain came through the roof.
7 He came top in the test. He scored fifty.
8 The goal came in the second minute. It was the only one to be scored.
9 The cake was not very good. I enjoyed the party.
10 Can't you wait. I have not finished my meal.

b Complete these sentences:

1 I went on the beach but . . .
2 The man fell off the roof but . . .
3 The carpet was cheap but . . .

4 The ghost appeared on Friday but . . .
5 The zoo was closed but . . .
6 I am younger than you but . . .
7 He jumped the stream but . . .
8 The lightning struck the golfer but . . .
9 She came off her bike but . . .
10 The police stopped his car but . . .

c Complete these sentences by adding a sentence to the front:

1 . . . but it did not matter.
2 . . . but I cannot help it.
3 . . . but it rained all day.
4 . . . but he was caught by the police.
5 . . . but the book did not have the answer.
6 . . . but she soon fell over.
7 . . . but it wore out quickly.
8 . . . but they were not the only ones.
9 . . . but the sun went in.
10 . . . but my mother did not tell me off.

Your own sentences

Write five of your own sentences, using *but*, about:

a match
a cooker
a tree
a disco
a monster

The complex sentence

17

Joining sentences – dependent clauses – because and if

'There are other useful words to join sentences,' said Mr Wright.

Take the sentence: I will not go out with him because I do not like him.

Because joins two sets of words: 'I will not go out with him' and 'I do not like him'. They could both be sentences on their own. They both have a verb with a time in it. But the word *because* belongs with 'I do not like him'. And 'because I do not like him' does not make complete sense on its own. So we can't call it a sentence. We give it a new name. We call a group of words like that a *clause*. We can also call it a *dependent clause* as it depends on another group of words to make complete sense sense.

Complete these by adding clauses of your own. In other word words, add a short sentence.

a Do this with Jim and Anne:

1 I will not go out because . . .
2 The match was cancelled because . . .
3 The prize was his because . . .
4 She was not afraid because . . .
5 The teacher was angry because . . .
6 The boy with the stammer fell out with his friend because . . .
7 She did not finish her homework because . . .
8 The family in the flat were poor because . . .
9 The new-born baby was crying because . . .

To vary your sentence pattern you can very often put the clause first:

Because I do not like him I will not go out with him.

Reverse the sentences you have just written.

Here are some *because* clauses. Add a sentence to them to make make one complete sentence.

b Do this with Jim and Anne:

1 . . . because it was raining.
2 . . . because I had a cold.
3 . . . because it was the end of the season.
4 . . . because I liked him.
5 . . . because the sun was shining.
6 . . . because of the time involved.
7 . . . because it looked too big to wear.
8 . . . because of the money it cost.
9. . . . because I could not stand the pain.

If is another common word to introduce clauses:

He would look nice, if he had a haircut.

Note how the *if* clause is separated by a comma.
Complete these *if* clauses.

c Do this with Jim and Anne:

1 I will go out, if . . .
2 The monster can be caught, if . . .
3 The eggs will not break, if . . .
4 She cannot help it, if . . .
5 It will be a disaster, if . . .
6 I will explain, if . . .
7 The house with the red roof will fall down, if . . .
8 The man with the limp will be cured, if . . .
9 The shop by the traffic lights will have to be closed, if . . .

Now reverse this sentence:

If he had a haircut, he would look nice.

Remember the comma.

Here are some *if* clauses. Add a sentence to them to make one complete sentence. Remember the comma.

d Do this with Jim and Anne:

1 . . . if we can spend all the money.
2 . . . if I can do it at my house.
3 . . . if the answer is correct.
4 . . . if the man in the red hat will listen.
5 . . . if there is room.
6 . . . if we want to go again.
7 . . . if the boy with the cough does not stop.
8 . . . if I can get my sums right.
9 . . . if the house by the river comes up for sale.

Now reverse each of those you have done. Remember the comma.

Your own sentences
Write five sentences of your own containing *because* clauses.
Write five sentences of your own containing *if* clauses.

Additional exercise
Complete these sentences:

1 He lost his job because . . .
2 The climber slipped down the mountain because . . .
3 She did not buy it because . . .
4 . . . because he would get into trouble.
5 . . . because it was a dangerous thing to do.
6 . . . because it was not built well enough.
7 The car will go off the road if . . .
8 You will not be allowed to go if . . .
9 The teacher is bound to be annoyed if . . .
10 . . . if I can help it.
11 . . . if you get them all right.
12 . . . if you do not have an injection.

18

Joining sentences – dependent clauses – so

'*So* is another common word to join sentences,' said Mr Wright, 'but like *and* and *but* it can be used too much. So use it sparingly.'

Complete the following by adding clauses of your own.

a Do this with Jim and Anne:

1 The match was called off so . . .
2 She had left the tickets at home so . . .
3 Someone had stolen his bike so . . .
4 Wayne had been coughing all night so . . .
5 Jayne could not come to the disco so . . .
6 The old tramp had no handkerchief so . . .
7 Steven missed the bus so . . .
8 The book was very dull so . . .
9 His bike still would not work so . . .
10 She could not find a clean blouse so . . .
11 No one was watching him so . . .
12 The shop was not making any money so . . .
13 It was a lovely day so . . .
14 The factory was bitterly cold so . . .
15 None of them had a sledge to use in the snow so . . .

Here are some *so* clauses. Add a sentence to them to make them into one sensible sentence.

b Do this with Jim and Anne:

1 . . . so she stayed at home.
2 . . . so the monkey threw the nuts back.
3 . . . so on Saturday I gave him a ring.

4 . . . so she fried herself an egg.
5 . . . so no one came to the party.
6 . . . so she cleaned all the windows in the house.
7 . . . so he hid behind a hedge.
8 . . . so she took a long time to open it.
9 . . . so it soon fell down.
10 . . . so the class were able to follow him.
11 . . . so he could breathe more easily.
12 . . . so the tank would have to stop.
13 . . . so it did no more damage.
14 . . . so she could get home as soon as possible.
15 . . . so he could have a good wage that week.

Your own sentences
Write five of your own sentences using *so*.

'*So that* is another useful way of adding clauses,' said Mr Wright.
She went to the doctor *so that* he could give her the prescription.
Complete the following by adding clauses of your own:

1 He stayed in so that . . .
2 The footballer crossed the ball so that . . .
3 She tied the bandage tightly so that . . .
4 The burglar climbed along the ledge so that . . .
5 The old gardener dug the ground carefully so that . . .
6 The stallholder set out his stall so that . . .
7 The motor-cyclist leaned right over so that . . .
8 The teacher helped the boy so that . . .
9 She stood on the box so that . . .
10 You must take the medicine so that . . .

19

Joining sentences – dependent clauses – when and where

'*Because* and *if* are two very common words to introduce clauses and join sentences but there are also many others,' said Mr Wright. 'I now want to show you some of the others you can use.'

I will go out *when* it stops raining.

Here the two sentences: 'I will go out' and, 'It stops raining' have been joined by *when*.

a Complete these sentences by adding a suitable clause:

1 I will go out when . . .
2 The fast car got out of control when . . .
3 The old man held on to the rail when . . .
4 It is best to give up when . . .
5 The cat burglar was surprised when . . .
6 The mossy wall fell down when . . .
7 The stall-holder with the big grin had a surprise when . . .
8 His step-mother fainted when . . .
9 Don't go out when . ...
10 She caught pneumonia when . . .

Now reverse any of the sentences which sound sensible, e.g.,

When it stops raining I will go out.

Remember! A clause is like a short sentence.

b Now put sentences in front of the *when* clauses:

1 . . . when I am seventeen.
2 . . . when I was young.

3 . . . when it happened all of a sudden.
4 . . . when the bird came down the chimney.
5 . . . when there are more of you.
6 . . . when the man with the plan comes.
7 . . . when my grandmother told me the truth.
8 . . . when he saw the lost treasure of the temple.
9 . . . when she let the cat out.
10 . . . when I dropped the money all over the floor.

Now reverse any that sound sensible.

Where is also another common joining word.

c Add a sensible clause to these:

1 Do not walk where . . .
2 I saw a body where . . .
3 There were many walkers where . . .
4 There is a wreck where . . .
5 I hope you can see where . . .
6 Can you see where . . .?
7 They put the cross where . . .
8 He went to the town where . . .
9 Is it the shop where . . .?
10 They saw the ghost in the place where . . .

Did you punctuate the two questions?

Reverse any that sound sensible.

d Now add sentences to the beginning of these:

1 . . . where the water came in.
2 . . . where my father died.
3 . . . where we are going.
4 . . . where the chickens were hatched.
5 . . . where my mother was staying.
6 . . . where there are no people.
7 . . . where I would like to go for my holiday.
8 . . . where it always seems to rain.
9 . . . where the sun always shines.
10 . . . where I caught the flu.

Now reverse any that sound sensible.

20

Joining sentences – dependent clauses – until, though or although and before

'Another useful word is *until*. Be careful to add a sentence and not just a word or a phrase,' said Mr Wright.

I cannot get one *until* I have saved up the money.

a Now do these with Jim and Anne:

1 You will have to wait in the room until . . .
2 There can be no prize given until . . .
3 The bus-conductor stood on the step until . . .
4 Do not enter the house until . . .
5 He will not give in until . . .
6 She ran and ran until . . .
7 The climbers walked over the mountain until . . .
8 I hope you will not do it until . . .
9 The tramp on the park seat did not get up until . . .
10 There cannot be peace until . . .

Reverse any that sound sensible.

b Now add a sentence before these:

1 . . . until I can do it.
2 . . . until we get home.
3 . . . until I have investigated the murder.
4 . . . until she sees his mother.
5 . . . until I am better.
6 . . . until the next time it happens.
7 . . . until the car by the lamp-post is moved.
8 . . . until I see the headmaster.
9 . . . until there are more of us.
10 . . . until I can get some money.

Now reverse any of these that sound sensible.

Another useful joining word is *although* or *though.*

c Complete these sentences:

1 He did not go out although . . .
2 She was determined to get into the show although . . .
3 The man did not move though . . .
4 The singer gave an encore although . . .
5 The policeman arrested the man though . . .
6 The fence fell down although . . .
7 He went in to the burning building though . . .
8 She still caught a cold although . . .
9 The doctor did not come although . . .
10 The judge did not send the criminal to prison although . . .

Now reverse any that sound sensible.

d Add a sentence to these:

1 . . . though it was raining.
2 . . . although he could not see the pitch.
3 . . . although she had never been there before.
4 . . . though he could not find the ring.
5 . . . although she was the best in the class.

e Another useful joining word is 'before'.
Complete these by adding a clause:

1 He had to take a great deal of medicine before . . .
2 You had better finish it before . . .
3 He was twelve years old before . . .
4 She dare not go down the corridor before . . .
5 He left the cinema before . . .
6 You had better leave the room before . . .
7 You must not set off on the journey before . . .
8 It is best to check the timetable before . . .
9 She took off her boots before . . .
10 It was three weeks before . . .

Check carefully that you have added a sentence and not a word or phrase. Then reverse any that sound sensible.

f Now add a sentence to these:
1 . . . before I tell your mother.
2 . . . before it is too late.
3 . . . before something happens to me.
4 . . . before I get very cross.
5 . . . before I could stop it.

Reverse any that sound sensible.

Your own sentences
Write fifteen sentences using any of these words: until, though, although, before.

Additional exercise
Join these two sentences together using either, 'until', 'though' or 'although', or 'before' as suitable:

1 Walk five miles. You come to a house with an enormous barn by it.
2 The young boy was very nervous. He went to the interview.
3 He was very wise. He was very young.
4 He twisted the villain's arm. It hurt.
5 It is very dangerous. It looks quite harmless.
6 He decided to buy a new car. It would have been wiser to wait until August.
7 You must learn to walk. You can run.
8 I cannot help you. I would like to do so.
9 No one will leave the room. The detective has come to a decision.
10 The garden was in a mess. I tidied it up.

21

Joining sentences – dependent clauses – as and as if, unless, after

'There are still more words,' said Mr Wright. 'They all make the language more interesting. *As* and *as if* are some more.'

He looked at the drawing *as if* he did not like it.
The pain hurt him *as* he sat down.

a Add a sentence before these clauses;

1 . . . as he had always done.
2 . . . as soon as his father got home.
3 . . . as the going was very rough.
4 . . . as she could not help it.
5 . . . as there was no reason to punish him.
6 . . . as I was going there anyway.
7 . . . as she had too many of them.
8 . . . as he had not caught any fish.
9 . . . as there was no money left.
10 . . . as painful as it had ever been.

Reverse any that sound sensible.

b Now add a sentence to these:

1 The blow to the face was as if . . .
2 She looked as if . . .
3 He walked round the room as if . . .
4 The car came round the corner as if . . .
5 The teacher said it seemed as if . . .
6 The Christmas tree looked as if . . .
7 The new record sounded as if . . .
8 The room looked as if . . .
9 The two boys from the end of the street jumped over the

wall as if . . .
10 The wife felt as if . . .

'Another word is *unless*, said Mr Wright.

You cannot do it *unless* you learn the proper way.

c Add a sentence to these:

1 You cannot find it unless . . .
2 It will not be possible to go unless . . .
3 You will not be able to open the window unless . . .
4 You will go to prison unless . . .
5 I cannot help you unless . . .

Reverse any that sound sensible.

d Put a sentence in front of these clauses:

1 . . . unless I am much mistaken.
2 . . . unless you give me some of them.
3 . . . unless you get here first.
4 . . . unless you pay the full amount.
5 . . . unless you buy a new one.

A further word is *after*.

The streets looked very wet *after* the rain had fallen.

e Be careful to add a clause to these and not a single word or a phrase.

1 He had three stitches in his head after . . .
2 The worker was dismissed after . . .
3 There were six of them in the river after . . .
4 She decided to go the other way after . . .
5 They found oil after . . .

Reverse any that sound sensible.

Your own sentences
Write fifteen of your own sentences using any of these words: as as, as if, after (be sure you have a verb with a time following the word *after*).

22

Joining sentences – dependent clauses – whether and while

'Still more words to go,' said Mr Wright. '*Whether* is a very common one.'

I do not know *whether* he knows the answer.

a Add a clause to these:

1 I cannot tell whether . . .
2 She did not know whether . . .
3 The policeman on the beat could not decide whether . . .
4 It does not matter to me whether . . .
5 The big mystery was whether . . .
6 She could not think whether . . .
7 The mountaineers could not make up their minds whether . . .

b Put a clause in front of these:

1 . . . whether the monster would attack him or not.
2 . . . whether to eat as much as he could.
3 . . . whether they would win the match.
4 . . . whether it would be better to stay at home.
5 . . . whether he wanted to go to the match.
6 . . . whether it would get better.
7 . . . whether he could get past the car.

c Now use *while*. Be careful to add a clause after *while* and not just a word or a phrase.

1 You must not move it while . . .
2 He did not want to go to London while . . .

3 The hypnotist watched while . . .
4 The jockey fell off while . . .
5 The tramp in the dirty raincoat sat on the seat while . . .
6 He could not like her while . . .
7 They sat in the dark while . . .
8 The nurses held the patient down while . . .

Reverse any that sound sensible.

d Add a sentence to these:

1 . . . while the policeman was there.
2 . . . while there was still time.
3 . . . while the fire burned out.
4 . . . while he caught four fish.
5 . . . while it was raining.
6 . . . while the man from the Council was there.
7 . . . while I eat another cake.
8 . . . while I fill up the car with petrol.

Your own sentences
Write fifteen of your own sentences using *whether* or *while.*

23
Joining sentences – dependent clauses – how and why

'You probably know,' said Mr Wright, 'that *how* and *why* are words that come at the beginning of a question. But they can also be used as words to introduce clauses.'

She did not know *why* she couldn't face the washing-up.
We all knew *how* he had done it so easily.

As with the other introductory words we can see them joining up clauses.

a Add a clause to these:

1 I don't know how . . .
2 John did not understand how . . .
3 She could not tell how . . .
4 He did not realise how . . .
5 She could not see how . . .
6 It began to dawn on her how . . .
7 The teacher could not think how . . .
8 The detectives never knew how.. . .

b Add a clause to these:

1 . . . how he was ever going to get there.
2 . . . how the film would end.
3 . . . how he could finish the meal.
4 . . . how she got there.
5 . . . how the dog got in the bedroom.

c Add a clause to these:

1 She could not tell why . . .

2 There seemed to be no reason why . . .
3 I do not see why . . .
4 His grandfather could not think why . . .
5 The teacher could not explain why . . .

d Add a clause to these:

1 . . . why he had never done it before.
2 . . . why she had not heard the record before.
3 . . . why it had happened to him.
4 . . . why they had lost.
5 . . . why she felt so happy now.

Your own sentences
Write five sentences using *how* and five using *why. Do not write questions.*

Additional exercise
Join up these clauses using 'how' or 'why' as suitable. Say which of them might be suitable for either word:

1 I cannot understand . . . you were not picked.
2 Can you give me an explanation . . . it came to be here?
3 You would not believe . . . it happened.
4 The policeman was surprised . . . the prisoner had escaped.
5 The experienced golfer was amazed . . . his partner sank the putt.
6 She did not understand . . . she did not get any better.
7 He did not see . . . he could not knit as well as a girl.
8 She went to find out . . . her father had been.
9 Let us learn . . . we can pass the test.
10 The magistrates could not discover . . . the woman had shop-lifted.

24

Joining sentences – dependent clauses – who

'Up till now we have just seen how you could use a word to join two sentences together,' said Mr Wright. 'Now I want you to look at ways of joining sentences together by making slight alterations.'

Who clauses are one of the commenest ways of doing this and they are very useful to help you vary your sentence pattern. Look at these two sentences:

He is just that kind of man. He gets angry very easily.

Here we have two sentences about the same person. You can use *who* to join the sentences together thus:

He is just that kind of man *who* gets angry very easily.

The second *he* has been taken out of the sentence and replaced by *who*. Note that the last word of the first sentence and the first word of the second sentence must be about the same person or people.

Now join these sentences together by using *who*.

Do this with Jim and Anne:

1 He had a row with his father. His father was very cross.
2 Barton Rovers have some good players. They will do even better next season.
3 Jack has a new girl friend. She is a champion swimmer.
4 Take a look at this strange old woman. She is standing at the bus-stop.
5 I am going to see my cousin. He is older than me.
6 She was sent to see the headmaster. He told her off.
7 Very soon he would see the runners. They were coming over the crest of the hill.

8 I do not like my uncle. He makes sarcastic remarks all the time.
9 He soon saw the policeman. He was making notes in his book.
10 He smiled at the shop assistant. She was dealing with a difficult customer.
11 The old woman complained to the doctor. He was very patient with her.
12 He could not find her in the crowd. They were getting very noisy.
13 The trainer ran quickly to the player. He was rolling around in agony.
14 The decorator dropped a pot of paint on his apprentice. He was knocked off the ladder.
15 The general inspected the soldiers. They looked very well turned-out.
16 What is the name of that teacher? She came last term. (Be careful about the question mark.)
17 The woman was very annoyed with the butcher. He had given her tough meat again.
18 The pedestrian shouted at the driver. He had nearly knocked him down on the crossing.
19 A tree fell on the forester. He had been very careless.
20 Robin Hood killed a deer for his merry men. They drank to his health.

Your own sentences

Write ten *who* sentences of your own. *Do not write questions.*

25
Joining sentences – dependent clauses – which and that

'*Which* is used in just the same way as *who*,' said Mr Wright, 'except that it is used for animals and things which are not human. *That* is used in the same way.'

Take the two sentences:

He caught his foot on a stone. It was sticking up from the path.

This can become:

He caught his foot on a stone *which* was sticking up from the path.*

or He caught his foot on a stone *that* was sticking up from the path.

Notice how 'it' refers to the 'stone' which is the last word in the first sentence.

Join up these sentences using *which* or *that*.

Do this with Jim and Anne:

1 The teacher picked up the book. It had a page torn out of it.
2 I could now see the lights. They were shining from the windows of the house.
3 The vet inspected the cattle. They had foot and mouth disease.
4 The tree swayed in the wind. It had been blowing hard all night.
5 Jim was chasing the monster. It was afraid of him despite its size.
6 The lightning struck the tent. It burst into flames.

*Modern English makes little distinction between 'which' and 'that'.

7 The hill farmer was looking for his sheep. They had strayed to the other side of the moor.
8 The girl tried to catch the horse. It had thrown her and galloped away.
9 She loved to go to the market. It had all sorts of different stalls.
10 There was something odd about the clock. It kept striking thirteen.
11 It was a ghost. It appeared at two in the morning and walked through walls.
12 In town was a splendid Christmas tree. It was all lit up with fairy lights.
13 My uncle owns a car. It is always breaking down.
14 He was always smoking. It damaged his health in the end.
15 Here is the bag. It was left on the chair in the other room.
16 They were struck half way up the cliff. It was a dangerous place to be.
17 The secret agent walked carefully down the lonely street. It was lit by only one lamp.
18 She had bad toothache. It had been hurting her all day.
19 She got her hand trapped in the washing machine. It was badly made.
20 There is the splinter. It was causing your thumb to fester.

Your own sentences

Write ten *which* or *that* sentences of your own. *Do not write questions.*

26
Joining sentences – dependent clauses – whose

'*Whose* is a useful word,' said Mr Wright. 'We use it when we mention a person at the end of the first sentence and when something which belongs to him or her begins the second sentence.'

Take these two sentences:

I met a man. His house caught fire.

This becomes:

I met a man *whose* house caught fire.

Do this with Jim and Anne:

1 I saw the girl. Her hair was dyed green.
2 The policeman caught the criminal. His fingerprints were all over the safe.
3 The referee spoke to the player. His tackle had broken the leg of the striker.
4 I had a row with the foreman. His temper was well-known throughout the factory.
5 The lord spoke to the butler. His drunkenness was getting worse.
6 I gave a list of faults on the car to the mechanic. His knowledge of engines was the best in the garage.
7 I spoke to the girl. Her dog was lost.
8 The traffic warden went up to the man. His car was parked on the double yellow lines.
9 In town I bumped into a friend of mine. His leg was in plaster.
10 My mother put up the next door neighbours. Their house had been flooded by a burst pipe.

Your own sentences
Write ten *whose* sentences of your own. *Do not write questions.*

27

Joining sentences – who, which and whose – another method

'Where we have two sentences with the same person or thing as the subject we use another method,' said Mr Wright.

Take these two sentences:

The boy was best at maths. He did badly in the exam.

This could be joined as:

The boy *who* was best at maths did badly in the exam.

Notice that 'The boy' and 'He', the subjects of the two sentences, are the same person. The word *who* is put behind the subject of the first sentence. The subject word of the second sentence is then cut out so 'He' disappears.

a Do this with Jim and Anne:

1 The girl sat on a log. She fell over backwards.
2 The sailor sailed the Atlantic single-handed. He took fifty days to cross.
3 A tall man was at the back of the crowd. He saved an old lady from falling.
4 The postman calls on Wednesdays and Thursdays. He has a limp.
5 The Littlewoods Pools agent knocked at the door. He was bringing a cheque for a hundred thousand pounds.
6 The Lord of the Manor was up early. He was shooting pheasants.
7 The leading goalscorer missed a penalty. He was dropped for the next match.
8 The doctor rushed to the scene of the accident at one in the morning. He saved the life of the motor-cyclist.

9 The Indian chief was an attraction to tourists. He was dressed in full war costume.
10 The TV repair man called on the pensioner. He mended his set for nothing.

' 'Which' can be used in the same way as 'who' if you are writing about animals or things,' said Mr Wright. 'Take the two sentences:

The house was flooded by the storm. It had its floorboards replaced.

This could become:

The house which was flooded in the storm had its floorboards replaced.

b Now do these examples:'

1 The fish swam in the deep pool by the willow. It never took the angler's bait.
2 The station has been closed down. It was built a hundred years ago.
3 The pylon was nearly finished. It would carry electricity to the village.
4 The lion was hunting. It was after fallow deer.
5 The castle was in danger. It could soon fall into the sea.
6 The doctor's surgery was crowded. It would have to be made bigger.
7 The book was a best-seller. It had sold over a million copies.
8 The pirate radio station has closed down. It was raided by Post Office engineers.
9 The motor-cycle helmet was banned by the Ministry. It had been the cause of several deaths.
10 The Easter egg was melting in the hot sun. It was in the shop window.

c Join these together using 'who' or 'which':

1 The doctor had been up all night. He arrived too late to save the dying man.
2 The elephant had sprayed water over the keeper. It was being taken back to the zoo.

3 The wrestler was thrown out of the ring. He had not trained properly.
4 The back axle was broken. It had only been bought yesterday.
5 The canoeist had passed the rough water. He had only two miles to go.

Whose can be used in the same way. You will notice, however, that the subject always has something owned in it and the possessive apostrophe will be used. Look at these two sentences:

The boy's leg was caught in a trap. He struggled to get free.

This becomes:

The boy whose leg was caught in a trap struggled to get free.

Note how the possessive apostrophe has disappeared in the joining.

d Now join these:

1 The girl's handbag was on a chair. She was kept talking by the thief's accomplice.
2 The girl's bike had been stolen. She phoned the police.
3 The parachutist's harness caught in the top of the tree. She was stuck there all night.
4 The woman's house was up for sale. She was emigrating to Australia.
5 The disc jockey's voice grated on my ear. He had been talking for three hours without a stop.

Your own sentences
Write ten sentences using *who*, *which* or *whose*, using the same pattern of the sentences you have been joining.

28
Joining sentences – dependent clauses – whom

'There is confusion in English about the use of the word *whom*,' said Mr Wright. 'Indeed, some writers ignore it altogether and use *who* always. It has the same linking function as *who* in that it joins sentences.'

Look at this example:

The teacher punished the girl. She cried a great deal.

This becomes:

The girl, whom the teacher punished, cried a great deal.

Note how the last words of the first sentence (a person) have become the first part of the new joined sentence. The person which the verb does something to is called the object. If this object starts the new sentence *whom* is used.

Join these sentences using 'whom' (note the commas in the example):

1 The manager told off the player. He gave in his notice.
2 My father helped a man. He was a friend of his.
3 The walker rescued the caver. He was trapped in an old mine shaft.
4 The warden reported the motorist. He was fined two hundred pounds.
5 The girl kissed the stranger. He was amazed.
6 The angry woman scolded the child. She burst into tears.
7 The landlord threw out the drunkard. He collapsed in the gutter.
8 The chef served the customer. She was very pleased.
9 The postman assisted the old lady. She was carrying a heavy shopping bag.

10 The hairdresser scalded the customer. She never went there again.

Here is another way of using 'whom':

This is the man. I will help him.

becomes

This is the man whom I will help.

Note how the subject 'I' comes after the 'whom'.

Now join these:

1 There were ten runners. He had coached them.
2 She lectured the pupils. She had chosen them.
3 There were ten workers. He wanted to sack them.
4 He went out with this girl. He loved her greatly.
5 They rescued the diver. They thought he had drowned.
6 There was this bus-driver. She dare not let him down.
7 He is the one. I wanted to help him.
8 There is the actor. I thought he acted best.
9 These are the players. He will praise them.
10 She caught up with the milkman. She was chasing him.

Your own sentences

Write five *whom* sentences of your own.

29

Joining sentences – the present participle

'In sentences where two things are happening at the same time we often do not use a joining word at all. We end the verb in the first sentence with -ing. Thus the verb *rushed* becomes *rushing*, said Mr Wright.

Look at these two sentences:

The woman rushed to the door. She knocked over a table.

This becomes:

Rushing to the door, the woman knocked over a table.

Note the comma and how the subject moves its position in the sentence. Join up these sentences using the present participle method:

1 The travellers trekked through the jungle. They were overcome by the heat.
2 The new tank rattled down the street. It fired right and left.
3 The schoolboy ran for the No 73 bus. He tripped over and cut his knee.
4 She rushed to get the dress finished. She sewed it up the wrong way.
5 He parked the car too quickly. He backed into a concrete post.
6 She jumped over the bar which had been raised a centimetre. She broke the school record.
7 She felt a migraine coming on. She went to bed at once.
8 The detective saw the man who had followed him in Oxford Street. He quickly went down the Underground station. (Do not make this 'sawing'.)
9 He strolled along the beach. He saw a bottle with a message in it.

10 The villain laughed in a dastardly way. He chained the heroine to the railway line.

Remember: the first part of the sentence you have made is not a sentence as there is no time in the verb.

Make these into complete sentences:

1 Leaping in the car, he . . .
2 Stealing the silver, the crooked butler . . .
3 Keeping care not to be seen, the infantryman . . .
4 Finding that she was last, the new girl . . .
5 Punching him in the face, the boxer . . .
6 Bleeding from the mouth, the shop-keeper . . .
7 Sitting firmly on the seat, my grandmother . . .
8 Grasping the long sword in both hands, the knight . . .
9 Gossiping with the neighbours, my friend . . .
10 Flinging the door shut, my auntie . . .

Your own sentences
Use these ten present participles to write sentences of your own:

hurrying skipping shouting falling going keeping
pushing helping turning forgetting

Joining three sentences

30
Joining three sentences – and

'Most people will join two sentences together naturally in speech, and fairly easily in writing if they are shown how,' said Mr Wright. 'Real skill, however, in writing comes when you can join three or more sentences together. I am going to concentrate now on joining more than two sentences together. Let's look back first at our old friend *and*.'

Look at these three sentences:

I sat down on the chair. I put my feet up. I went to sleep.

The temptation is to write:

I sat down on the chair and I put my feet up and I went to sleep.

But it is better to write:

I saw down on the chair, put my feet up and went to sleep.

Note how only one subject ('I') is used at the start and how the comma is used after the first sentence. One 'and' is used to join the last two sentences. This method of construction is used when you have three consecutive actions or three closely related facts.

Join these sentences together using this method:

1 I got on a bus. I paid my fare. I went to Birmingham.
2 He flopped down into the chair. He sat on a drawing pin. He jumped in the air.
3 The wrestlers jumped into the ring. They took off their dressing gowns. They grappled with each other.
4 The teacher walked in the classroom. He picked up the chalk. He wrote on the board.

5 The milkman went to the depot. He loaded his float. He set out on his rounds.
6 The batsman walked proudly to the wicket. He took a long time getting ready. He was out first ball.
7 The athlete crouched in her blocks. She waited for the gun. She got away like a rocket.
8 The policemen came out of the station. They got in the car. They chased after the bank robbers.
9 The wooden house caught fire. It burned all night. It was a heap of ashes in the morning.
10 The lion came out of the forest. It crawled along on its stomach. It sprang on its prey.

Your own sentences

Write five of your own sentences using this pattern. Use these subjects:

The yachtsman   The doctor   He   She   The runners

31

Joining three sentences – other methods

'I want you to take a look back to chapters 17-23 of this book,' said Mr Wright. 'Make a list of all the joining words used there. These words can also join three sentences together as well as two.'

Look at these sentences:

He had left the house. He stopped in the street. He heard a footstep behind him.

This could become:

After he had left the house, he stopped in the street *because* he had heard a footstep behind him.

Here *after* and *because* have both been used to make a longer complex sentence. (Note the comma.)

Use *while* and *because* to join these sentences:

The rain came down heavily. The walkers sheltered under a tree. They had left their macs behind.

Have your list of joining words in front of you. Use any two of them that sound sensible to join these groups of three sentences:

1 He drove the car. He put his seat belt on. He was afraid of accidents.
2 He was going too fast. He reached the corner. He came off his bike.
3 She was waiting for the bus. She read her textbook again. She wanted to do well in the test.
4 He heard a creak in the night. He hid under the bedclothes. He was afraid of ghosts.
5 The four men in front of him stood up. He shouted angrily.

He could not see the match.

6 There had been a lot of injuries in the game. The referee's whistle did not go. Full-time came.
7 He had slammed the door behind him. He checked his pockets. He thought he had forgotten the key.
8 He played the mouth organ. The dog howled. It hated the sound.
9 Her husband came into the room. She threw a pot at him. She was so angry.
10 She got to the station. She found she had missed the train. She had talked to so many people on the way.
11 He had a cold. His mother allowed him to play indoors. It was raining.
12 She did not know. She should go to the pictures. Her mother was ill.
13 I do not know. It does not work. I have looked at every part.
14 I go out. I always check to see. I have some money.
15 The house with white shutters will be sold. They can get the right price for it. The owners want to go to America.
16 He did not look. He was going. He was drunk.
17 I cannot tell. It will work at all. I have taken it to pieces.
18 You go swimming in the river. You should check that it is safe. You want to take a big risk.
19 The angry sea was pouring over the sandhills. The storm was at its height. At sea ships were sheltering in the bay.
20 The officer asked the troops to attack. They were under heavy fire. The hill had to be captured.
21 She was ill. She did not go to her mother's. It was her day to go.
22 He crawled under the car. He could get to the engine. He thought the fault was in the gear box.
23 I am doing the washing. Please take your dirty shirt off. I want to do it all.
24 You catch the 4.20 pm train. You will get to Brighton in time. You can visit the exhibition.
25 The porter looked at the woman. He could have killed her. She got on his nerves so much.
26 The AA man stopped on the hard shoulder of the M1. He was going to help a woman. Her car had broken down.
27 The owner of the greengrocer's shop ordered the Christmas

trees. He could make a lot of money. It was a risk to buy them so early.

28 I cannot put all my weight on my left foot. It hurts so much. I had an operation on it.

29 The manager of the tyre factory complained to the workers. They did not make enough tyres. The big demand for them came in the spring.

30 The estate agent swindled the young couple. He sold them a house with death-watch beetle in the roof. He assured them it was a good buy.

31 I cannot tell. It got like that. I have cleaned it every week.

32 The spring comes. We will go a long walk over the mountain. Your mother does not like the idea.

33 I go to bed. I always look under it. There might be someone hiding beneath it.

34 The scientist worked feverishly on the machine. He wanted to get it finished. He could rule the world.

35 You pay me. I will not finish the job. I know you need it done quickly.

36 They forgot all about the dangerous bend at the bottom of the hill. The road turned at right angles. They were in a hurry to get to the party.

37 The electricity workers scaled the pylon. A wire had snapped. The gale was at its height.

38 The night came upon them. They had to reach the shepherd's hut. It was the only place to shelter.

39 The clock struck twelve. Cinderella had to leave the ball. Her fairy godmother told her she must.

40 He knew he must leave the wood before midnight. A vampire might attack him. He found a hiding place.

Your own sentences

Write your own sentences using these words:

when, because	if, although
while, because	when, if
as, because	if, because
since, until	where, as
whether, as	if, unless

32

Joining three sentences – who and which

'You may also find *who* and *which* in the same sentence joining three sentences,' said Mr Wright.

Look at these examples:

The conductor conducted the orchestra. They were playing Elgar's music. They liked it very much.

This could become:

The conductor conducted the orchestra *who* were playing Elgar's music *which* they liked very much.

Take a look back at the two methods of using *who* and *which* and then look at this example:

The dog killed the sheep. It was destroyed by its owner. He hated doing it very much.

This could become:

The dog *which* killed the sheep was destroyed by its owner *who* hated doing it very much.

Now join these sentences using *who* and *which:*

1 The manager blamed the team. They were bottom of the league. It was being contested fiercely that year.
2 The house stood on the hill. It was being knocked down by the landowner. He said it spoiled his view.
3 My sister knows a girl. She likes visiting old houses. It gives them both some interesting days out.
4 The tramp is very cold. He is eating sandwiches. They were given to him by the cafe owner.
5 He bit the rugby forward. He had punched his face in the scrum. It had collapsed in the thick mud.

6 The overseer blamed the worker. She was late again. This was the third time this week.
7 The dam was in danger of collapsing. It was saved by the engineers. They worked all through the night.
8 She told him he was a menace. He needed to be locked up. This upset him a great deal.
9 The geologist struck oil. He was delighted. It made a big difference to his life.
10 The computer engineer invented a new machine. It could save the life of a man. He had been drowned.

It is also possible to use *who* twice in a sentence and *which* as well, though these kind of sentences are rarer. The following examples are of this kind:

11 The Titanic was supposed to be unsinkable. It struck an iceberg. This sunk it immediately.
12 The detective suspected the butler. He thought it was the housemaid. She had been following him about with an odd look on her face.
13 The fire-engine raced round the corner. It struck a traffic light. This fell on top of a passing car.
14 The batsman knocked up the ball to the wicket-kepper. He tipped it to first slip. He caught it at the second attempt.
15 The tide was rising all the time. It had cut off the village. This means the doctor could not reach the dying man.

Your own sentences
Write five sentences of your own using *who* and *which.*

33
Joining three sentences – a combination of methods

'Most long complex sentences use a combination of the methods we have shown,' said Mr. Wright.

Study these examples:

The man went home. He was angry. He wanted to complain to his wife.

This could become:

The man *who* was angry went home *because* he wanted to complain to his wife.

Or take the sentences:

He hoped for a lift. He thumbed a lorry. It went straight past him.

This could become:

Hoping for a lift, he thumbed a lorry *which* went straight past him.

Or take the sentences:

The sun was shining. He went out for a drive with his girlfriend. She was enjoying her twenty-first birthday.

This could become:

As the sun was shining, he went for a drive with his girlfriend *who* was enjoying her twenty-firth birthday.

Using a variety of methods join these sentences together. Do not use *and.*

Do this with Jim and Anne:

a In the first ten examples the joining words are given for you, but not necessarily in the right order.

1 It rains. Will you bring the washing in? It is nearly dry. (when, as)
2 He stopped at the paper shop. He bought *The Daily Telegraph.* He wanted to do the crossword. (because, stopping)
3 This is the house. I would like to buy it. It has such a nice garden. (which, as)
4 You mow the grass. Be sure to clean the mower. I have just bought. (when, which)
5 The barber cut the man's hair. He snipped his ear. This made the man jump in the chair. (which, as)
6 You must not complete the deal. You have consulted a solicitor. He knows about such matters. (until, who)
7 The sun was shining. He cleaned the car. It was very muddy. (as, while)
8 I do not know. I should report the hooligan to that man. He is standing by the ticket office. (whether, who)
9 My grandmother sat on the bed. She cut her toenails. They were very long. (which, sitting)
10 Please fix the sewing-machine. I can mend my jeans. They are badly torn. (which, so)

b In the next ten examples one joining word is given. You must find the other one.

1 I move the branch. You hold that one up. It is trapping me. (while, ?)
2 This is the woman. She found your purse. You left it at the butcher's. (which, ?)
3 You upset me so much. I will not give you the present. You have always wanted it. (as, ?)
4 The Loch Ness monster comes to the surface. Try and get a photo of it. We can sell it to the papers. (which, ?)
5 The man bought my old car. He went away happy. He had got a bargain. (because, ?)
6 The postman stopped by the gate. He sorted out the letters. They were for the Smith family. (which, ?)

7 He looked at me. He would not tell me again. The one I should choose. (as if, ?)
8 The cyclist slid across the path. He hit this man. He fell off his bike. (sliding, ?)
9 It is your turn. Do not play the record. I do not like it. (when, ?)
10 You must not turn the knob. You see the green light. It is by the figure seven. (until ?)

c Join up the sentences in the following twenty examples. Select from these joining words: who, which, if, as, where, since, when, because, while, after, -ing:

1 You have difficulty in hearing. I will not sell you this cassette recorder. It does not have a very loud volume.
2 I do not know. I have put my grandfather's letter. I received it last Thursday.
3 This is the girl. She likes her meat well-cooked. She cannot stand the sight of blood.
4 The driver stopped by the traffic lights. He hooted at the pedestrian. He had nearly walked under his car.
5 The man is sitting next to the touchline taking photos. He could get hurt soon. Most of the play is down that side of the field.
6 The house is next to the supermarket. It has a great problem. So many people park their cars in front of it.
7 You fetch the shopping from the corner shop. I will help our old auntie. She is very ill with arthritis in the legs.
8 You do not take the medicine. You will have a rash. It will cover your body from head to toe.
9 The potholer found the entrance to the cave. He took the route by the stalactite. It would help him to find his companion.
10 The storm passes over. We must set off for Oxford. It is still ten miles down the road.
11 You are ten. I think you are old enough to clean the kitchen. It is very dirty and smelly.
12 The engine driver stepped out of his cab. He was staggering all over the place. He had a serious illness.
13 The printer printed five hundred tickets for the dance. It would be held in the open air. The weather was fine.

14 The runner stopped to get his breath. He paused by the old oak tree. It was the halfway point of the race.

15 You will help your mother. You will not be allowed to see your friends. They will have to play with someone else for a change.

16 This is the man. He had a lucky escape from death. He touched a live electric cable.

17 The seagull came inland to feed. It had a bent leg. The weather had been so cold that year.

18 The operation he had for gallstones. He felt much better. This was a great relief to his wife.

19 The quiz contestant paused to guess the answer. He looked up at his wife. She was trying to signal to him from the audience.

20 It comes out fine. We will go to the park. It has just opened after alterations.

Your own sentences

Write your own sentences using these words:

who, because	which, as
which, if	who, while
who, when	which, until
which, because	helping, who
who, unless	learning, which

Joining four sentences

34

Joining four sentences – a combination of methods

'It is also possible to join four sentences together,' said Mr Wright. 'Once again it is better if we use a combination of methods. We are still trying to use *and*, *but* and *so* as infrequently as possible.'

Look at these examples:

The man went out. The clock struck twelve. He had a cold. It was raining.

This could become:

The man *who* had a cold went out *when* the clock struck twelve *although* it was raining.

Look at these sentences:

The team are at the bottom of the league. Their form is poor. They try hard. They will win the next match.

This could become:

The team *which* are at the bottom of the league *because* of their poor form will win the next match, *if* they try hard.

Note how in both examples the sentence order can change and slight changes can be made as in the second example.

And is still a useful word. But use it as sparingly as possible. Thus:

He helped himself to another piece of cake. It was on the table. He grinned. He made fun of his hostess.

This could become:

Helping himself to another piece of cake *which* was on the table he grinned *and* made fun of his hostess.

a Join these sentences together using the words given, but not necessarily in the order the joining words are given.

Do this with Jim and Anne:

1 The girl tried to listen to the radio. She was deaf. She had had much treatment. It was turned down. (who, although, which)
2 The river rises over the wall. It is at the bottom of the garden. Please ring up the police. Their number is 72205. (if, whose, which)
3 The person removed the desk lock. It had just been fixed. He wanted to get the paper. He must report to the office immediately. (because, who, which)
4 She turned round. She knocked over the vase. It was on top of the television. It looked nice there. (turning, which, as)
5 The arrow reaches the top of the dial. It is by the water pipe. Turn off the current. That is the danger point. (as, which, when)

b In the next five examples use the two joining words given and find one more of your own:

1 The boats are in the harbour. They must leave by dawn. The owners pay the increased fee. They are responsible. (which, unless, ?)
2 The oak tree must be cut down. It has stood for one hundred years. It is dangerous. It has had treatment (although, which, ?)
3 The doctor is a specialist in skin diseases. They attack the face. He has been in much demand. The poision escaped from the factory. (since, who, ?)
4 The cyclist stayed in the front. He had been leading the race. He kept his rivals in sight all the way up the hill. It was the steepest on the circuit. (staying, who, ?)
5 The full-back took the pass. It was given to him by the goalkeeper. He had come a long way out of his goal. He was taking a big risk. (who, and, ?)

c In the next ten examples only one joining word is given. You select the other two and join the sentences:

1 He was very young. His mother would not allow him to go out alone. It was dangerous. There had been a fight in the street. (since, ?, ?)
2 The house will be sold. It stands on the hill. The owner is going to Australia. He has two sons there. (where, ?, ?)
3 You come up with a better answer. You had better keep quiet. It will upset your father. He is not well today. (until, ?, ?)
4 He looked. A car had run him down. There were tyre marks on his jacket. It was also torn to bits. (as if, ?, ?)
5 She sat on the step. She felt humiliated. Her mother had treated her badly. She had not listened to her explanation. (sitting, ?, ?)
6 The engine was running. He looked under the bonnet. He found a piece of metal. It was causing the short. (and, ?, ?)
7 The eagle settled on the branch. It came from Scotland. It looked at the rabbit. It had just come out of its burrow. (settling, ?, ?)
8 The disc jockey started off with the number one disc. He was new to the programme. His grandmother had requested it. She was eighty. (because, ?, ?)
9 She trapped the ball. She passed it to her winger. She was coming up on her left. She was racing for goal. (and, ?, ?)
10 He hoped to hear good news. He picked up the phone. It rang loudly. It had just been repaired. (hoping, ?, ?)

d In the next thirty examples no joining words are given. Use some of the following words and methods to join the sentences. Try to vary your methods:

-ing, although, since, where, because, when, as if, whether, that, if, so, as, and, but, so, who, which, whose

1 It was twenty years. He had seen his friend. He had emigrated to New Zealand. He knew his face immediately.
2 He did not know. He had put it. His memory was a complete blank. He had had the accident.
3 The mountaineer gripped the rock. He was on his first Himalayan expedition. He inched up to the ledge. His fellow

climber was standing there.

4 It was Saturday morning. She did not want to get up. She did not want to go to work. She could have been lying in bed.

5 He slipped on the ice. He broke his leg. He was too mean to go by bus. He ended up in hospital.

6 This is the man. His cousin is in Australia. He farms sheep there. He keeps cattle there.

7 The smoke rose from the fire. This was a signal to the Indians. They lived in the valley. The Yellow River runs there.

8 He looked. He would fall off the ladder. My brother ran forward. He steadied it at the base.

9 You are so young. I will not punish you this time. Next time I will. Your father would be upset by such behaviour.

10 She did not know. Her sister was to be believed. She still did not doubt. She wanted to tell the truth.

11 The programme was boring all the family. They liked to watch television after tea. He switched over to see. There was nothing better on the other channel.

12 He overcame his fear of heights. He scaled the cliff. It hung over the inlet. He could reach his trapped brother.

13 You could never tell. He had an artificial leg. He did not walk with a limp. It was surprising.

14 The bottle of toffee had been there for years. It stood on the shelf in the post office. I often wondered. Should I risk buying any?

15 Don't feed the parrot. It is in the cage. It is not well. It has been in a draught.

16 I wish to go to Florida. Disneyland is there. I have always wanted to. I was a child.

17 Do you think. You could keep quiet. The baby kept me awake last night. I want a few minutes' sleep.

18 I would like to help you. I can't. You insist on doing it the wrong way. This will eventually break it.

19 The grandfather clock is worth a great deal of money. It has stood in the attic for years. It was made by craftsmen. They gave it to Queen Victoria.

20 I will not have an aspirin. It might send me to sleep. I want to stay up. I can watch the late-night news.

21 The egg was on the table. It fell off. His mother knocked it with a spoon. She was bending over the table to make the cake.

22 You must go to the library. You go to town. I want to borrow that new book. It has just been published.

23 The house is up for sale. It is by the river. The owner has only been in it five months. His son has died.

24 The surgeon operated on the patient. The surgeon had been up all night. The patient collapsed in the ward. He had appendicitis.

25 The river is high. You must not cross it. You might drown. You are not a strong swimmer.

26 The washing machine has broken down. My mother gave it to me. It was overloaded. Water went all over the kitchen floor.

27 She was going to the polling booth. She was approached by a man. He tried to make her vote for a particular candidate. It was against the law.

28 There was a dead branch on the tree. It needed to be removed. It might fall on the child. He tried to climb the tree.

29 He turned round the bend. He saw a highwayman. He menaced him with two pistols. They glinted in the moonlight.

30 He felt tired. He continued to work the lathe. The foreman had told him he must finish the job. He wanted a week off.

Your own sentences

Write four closely connected sentences. Ask your neighbour to join them together. Do this five times.